CHART HI

easy playalong *for* clarinet

WISE PUBLICATIONS
London/New York/Paris/Sydney/Copenhagen/Madrid/Tokyo

Exclusive Distributors:
Music Sales Limited
8/9 Frith Street,
London W1D 3JB, England.

Music Sales Pty Limited
120 Rothschild Avenue,
Rosebery, NSW 2018,
Australia.

Order No. AM967802
ISBN 0-7119-8537-5
This book © Copyright 2001 by Wise Publications.

Music arranged by CN Productions Ltd.
Music processed by Enigma Music Production Services.
Cover photography courtesy George Taylor.
Printed in the United Kingdom by
Printwise (Haverhill) Limited, Haverhill, Suffolk.

CD Engineered by Arthur Dick.
Instrumental solos by John Whelan.

Your Guarantee of Quality:
As publishers, we strive to produce every book to
the highest commercial standards.
The music has been freshly engraved and the book
has been carefully designed to minimise awkward page
turns and to make playing from it a real pleasure.
Particular care has been given to specifying acid-free,
neutral-sized paper made from pulps which have not
been elemental chlorine bleached.
This pulp is from farmed sustainable forests and
was produced with special regard for the environment.
Throughout, the printing and binding have been planned
to ensure a sturdy, attractive publication which should
give years of enjoyment.
If your copy fails to meet our high standards,
please inform us and we will gladly replace it.

Music Sales' complete catalogue describes
thousands of titles and is available in full colour
sections by subject, direct from Music Sales Limited.
Please state your areas of interest and send
a cheque/postal order for £1.50 for postage to:
Music Sales Limited, Newmarket Road,
Bury St. Edmunds, Suffolk IP33 3YB.

www.musicsales.com

Clarinet
Fingering Chart

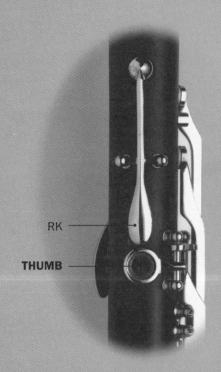

RK

THUMB

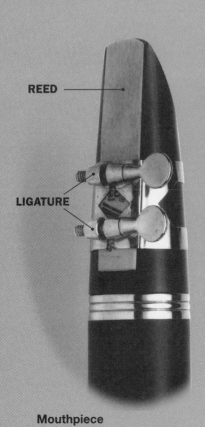

REED

LIGATURE

Mouthpiece

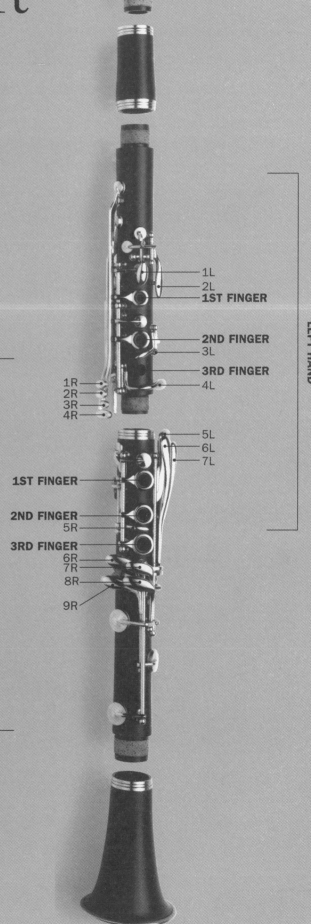

LEFT HAND

1L
2L
1ST FINGER

2ND FINGER
3L

3RD FINGER
4L

1R
2R
3R
4R

5L
6L
7L

RIGHT HAND

1ST FINGER

2ND FINGER
5R

3RD FINGER
6R
7R
8R

9R

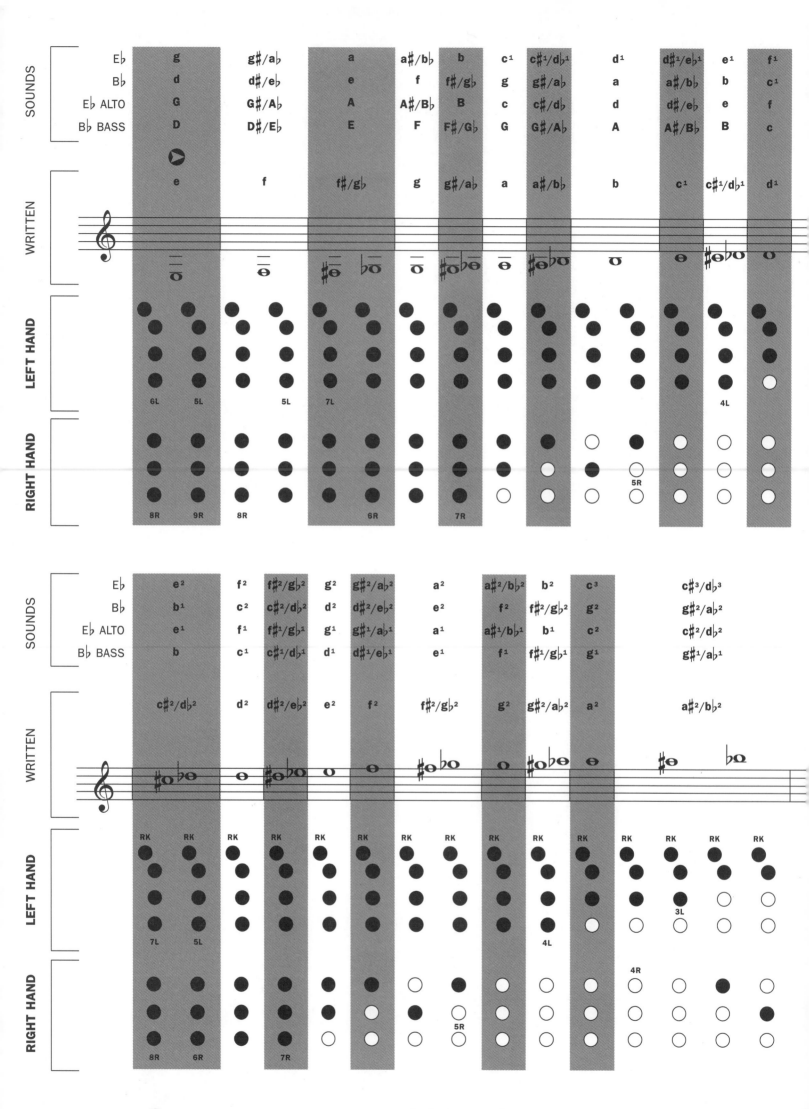

Indicates the lower limit of the best playing range for E♭, B♭, E♭ Alto and B♭ Bass Clarinets

f#¹/g♭¹   g¹   g#¹/a♭¹   a¹   a#¹/b♭¹   b¹   c²   c#²/d♭²   d²   d#²/e♭²

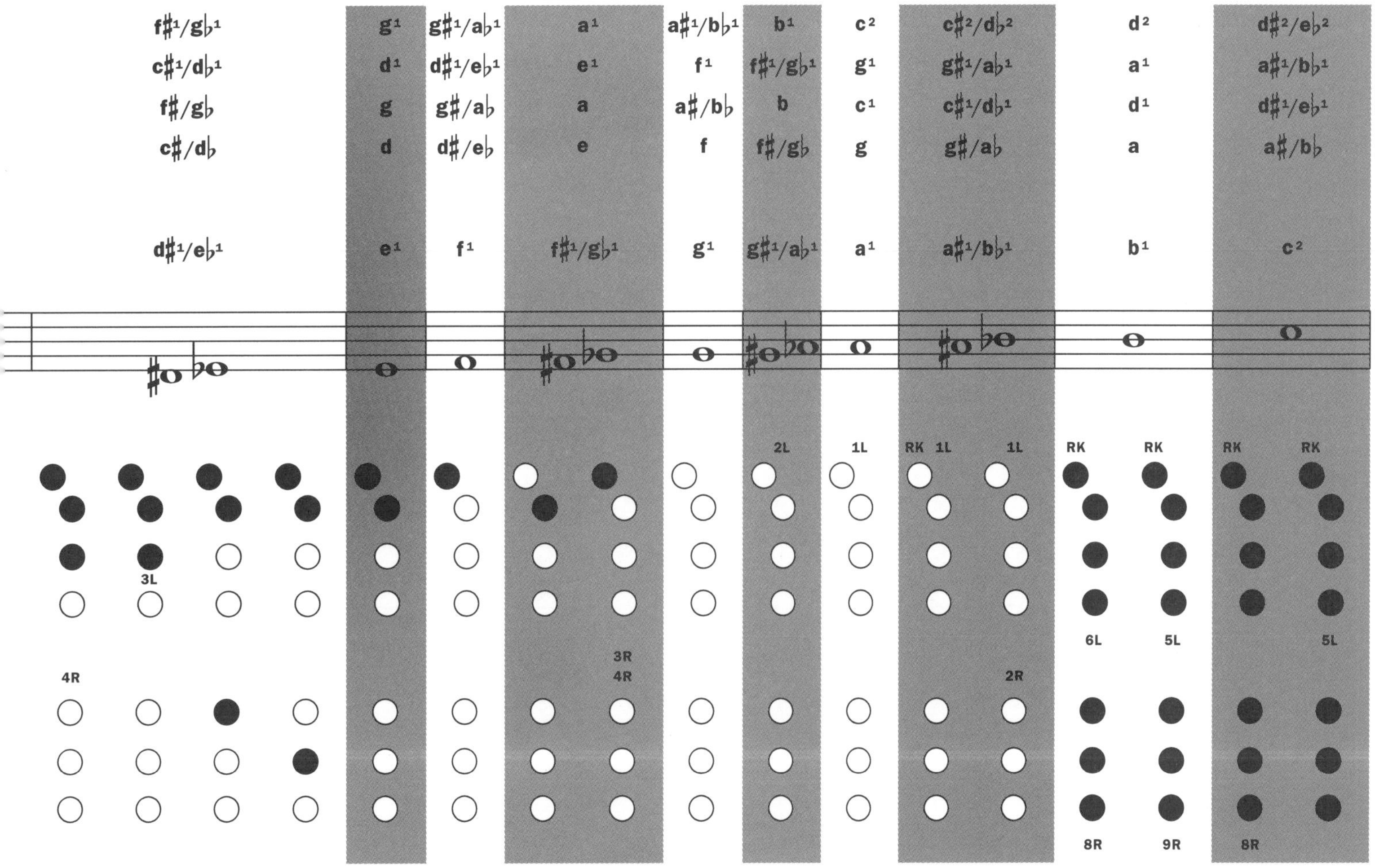

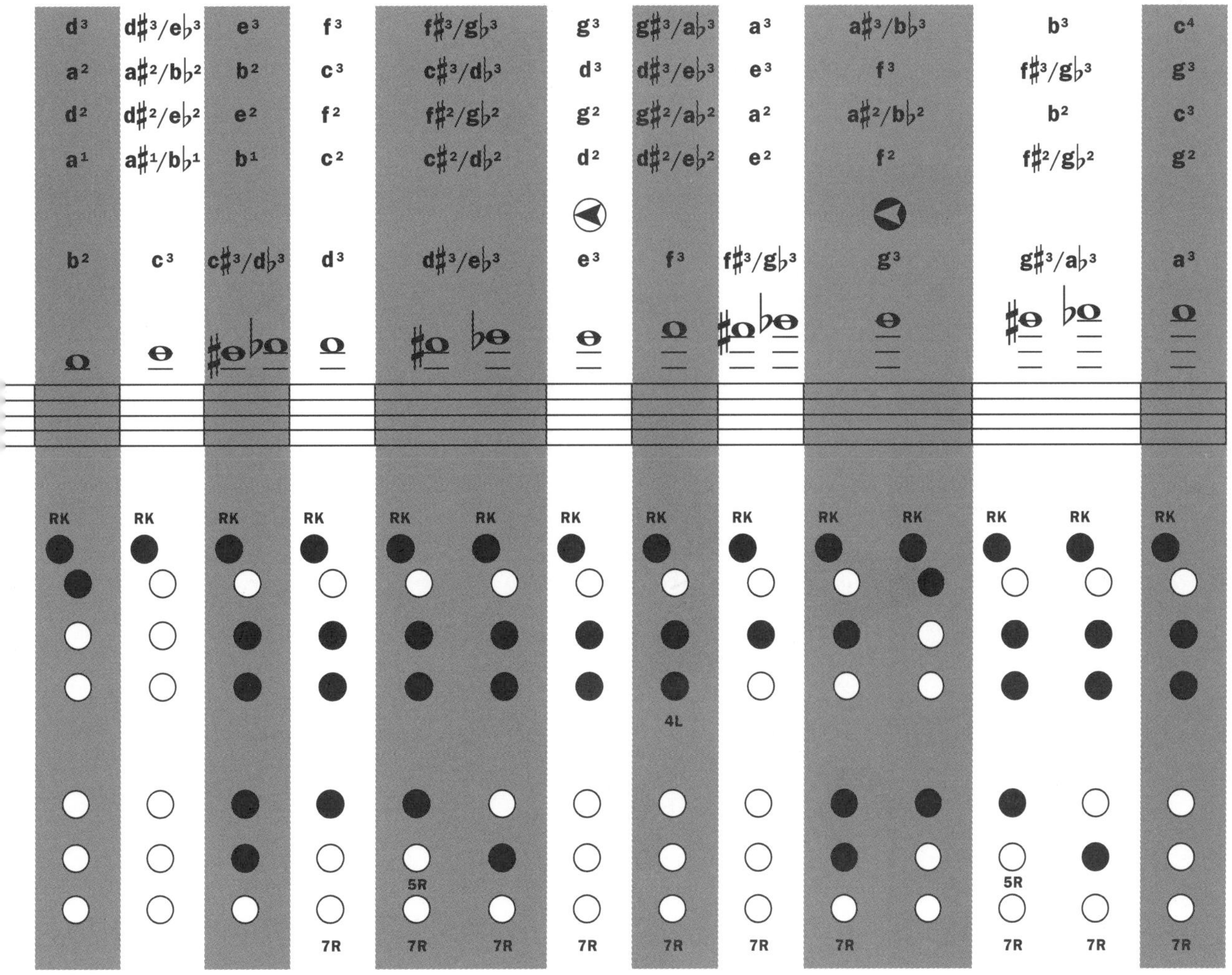

c#¹/d♭¹   d¹   d#¹/e♭¹   e¹   f¹   f#¹/g♭¹   g¹   g#¹/a♭¹   a¹   a#¹/b♭¹

f#/g♭   g   g#/a♭   a   a#/b♭   b   c¹   c#¹/d♭¹   d¹   d#¹/e♭¹

c#/d♭   d   d#/e♭   e   f   f#/g♭   g   g#/a♭   a   a#/b♭

d#¹/e♭¹   e¹   f¹   f#¹/g♭¹   g¹   g#¹/a♭¹   a¹   a#¹/b♭¹   b¹   c²

Fingering labels (top chart): 2L, 1L, RK, 1L, 1L, RK, RK, RK, RK, 3L, 4R, 3R, 4R, 2R, 6L, 5L, 5L, 8R, 9R, 8R

---

d³   d#³/e♭³   e³   f³   f#³/g♭³   g³   g#³/a♭³   a³   a#³/b♭³   b³   c⁴

a²   a#²/b♭²   b²   c³   c#³/d♭³   d³   d#³/e♭³   e³   f³   f#³/g♭³   g³

d²   d#²/e♭²   e²   f²   f#²/g♭²   g²   g#²/a♭²   a²   a#²/b♭²   b²   c³

a¹   a#¹/b♭¹   b¹   c²   c#²/d♭²   d²   d#²/e♭²   e²   f²   f#²/g♭²   g²

b²   c³   c#³/d♭³   d³   d#³/e♭³   e³   f³   f#³/g♭³   g³   g#³/a♭³   a³

Fingering labels (bottom chart): RK (repeated across columns), 4L, 5R, 7R

Indicates the upper limit of the best playing range for E♭ and B♭ Clarinets

Indicates the upper limit of the best playing range for E♭ Alto and B♭ Bass Clarinets

AMERICAN PIE

Words & Music by Don McLean

BLACK COFFEE

Words & Music by Tom Nichols, Alexander Soos & Kirsty Elizabeth

BREATHLESS

Words & Music by R. J. Lange, Andrea Corr, Caroline Corr, Sharon Corr & Jim Corr

Moderately

IT FEELS SO GOOD

Words & Music by Sonique, Linus Burdick & Simon Belofsky

MY LOVE

Words & Music by Jörgen Elofsson, Pelle Nylén, David Kreuger & Per Magnusson

NATURAL BLUES

Words by Vera Hall
Music by Vera Hall & Moby
'Natural Blues' is based on the song 'Trouble So Hard' (Words & Music by Vera Hall)

REACH

Words & Music by Cathy Dennis & Andrew Todd

When the world leaves_you feel - ing blue, you_ can count on me, I___ will be there for you. When it seems, all___ your hopes and dreams are a mil - lion miles a - way I___ will re - assu - re you. We got to all___ stick to - ge - ther good friends there___ for each oth -er, nev - er ev - er for - get that I got you and you got me so... Reach for the

stars,   climb ev - 'ry moun - tain high - er.   Reach   for the

stars,   fol - low your hearts de - sire,___ reach   for the

stars,   and when that rain - bow's shi - ning ov - er you___

___ that's when your dreams_will all_ come,   reach   for the

stars,   climb ev - 'ry moun-tain high - er.   Reach   for the

stars,   fol - low your hearts de - sire,___ reach   for the

stars,   and when that rain - bow's shi - ning ov - er you___

___ that's when your dreams_will all_ come true.

17

RISE

Words & Music by Bob Dylan, Gabrielle, Ferdy Unger-Hamilton & Ollie Dagois

SHAPE OF MY HEART

Words & Music by Max Martin, Rami & Lisa Miskovsky

STOMP

Words & Music by Mark Topham, Karl Twigg & Rita Campbell

Thank God for the week - end, now is the time, for feel - in' al - right come and taste the spice of life. To - night no - thin' mat - ters come feel the groove. Let it in to you you know what you got to do. Ev - 'ry Fri - day when my work is done and I get my par - ty on I call a few friends of mine make sure I'm look - ing fine.

STRONGER

Words & Music by Max Martin & Rami

SUPREME

Words & Music by Robbie Williams, Guy Chambers, Dino Fekaris & Frederick Perren

WALKING AWAY

Words & Music by Craig David & Mark Hill

Slowly

I'm walk-ing a-way, ___ from the trou-bles in my life, I'm walk-ing a-way ___ oh to find a bet-ter day. I'm walk-ing a-way ___ from the trou-bles in my life, I'm walk-ing a-way, ___ oh to find a bet-ter day. I'm walk-ing a-way. ___ Some-times, ___ some peo-ple get me wrong ___ when it's some-thing I've said or done. ___ Some-times ___ you feel ___ there is no fun ___ that's why you turn and run. ___ But now I tru-ly re-a-lise, ___

THE WAY YOU MAKE ME FEEL

Words & Music by Phil Thornalley & Bryan Adams

I'M OUTTA LOVE

Words & Music by Anastacia, Sam Watters & Louis Biancaniello

1/02 (42386)